Zaner-Bloser
Handwriting

fly

ZB **Zaner-Bloser**

Credits

Art: Mircea Catusanu/Painted Words: 10, 110, 112, 114, 116–118, 120, 122, 124, 125, 132–135, 140, 141; Bob Masheris/Wilkinson Studios: 16, 18, 20–22, 25–28; Gary Krejca/Wilkinson Studios: 30, 34–41; Nancy Gayle Carlson/Painted Words: 42–47, 67, 77, 85; Bernard Adnet/Craven Design: 50, 52, 54, 56, 58–60, 62, 64, 66, 70, 72, 74, 76, 78, 80, 82, 84; Tim Beaumont/Painted Words: 88, 90, 92, 94, 96, 98, 100, 102, 104, 106; John Hovell: 142

Literature: "Signposts" by Vivian Gouled, from *Houghton Mifflin Reading*, ©1971. Published by Houghton Mifflin Harcourt Publishing Company. All rights reserved.; "Clouds" by Aileen Fisher. Permission pending from Marian Reiner.

Photos: ©Jim Zuckerman/Corbis: Cover; George C. Anderson Photography, Inc.: 5, 12–15; ©STONEIMAGES/Photolibrary: 6–7; ©Comstock/Getty Images: 32–33; ©Don Farrall/Getty Images: 48–49; ©iStockphoto.com/hartcreations: 69; ©iStockphoto.com/Juanmonino: 87; ©iStockphoto.com/Saphra: 109; ©Siri Stafford/Getty Images: 127; ©Dave Nagel/Getty Images: 128–129

Zaner-Bloser

CONTENTS

Unit 4 Using What You Have Learned

We like to write!

This book will help you write.
You will learn to make your writing
easy for others to read.

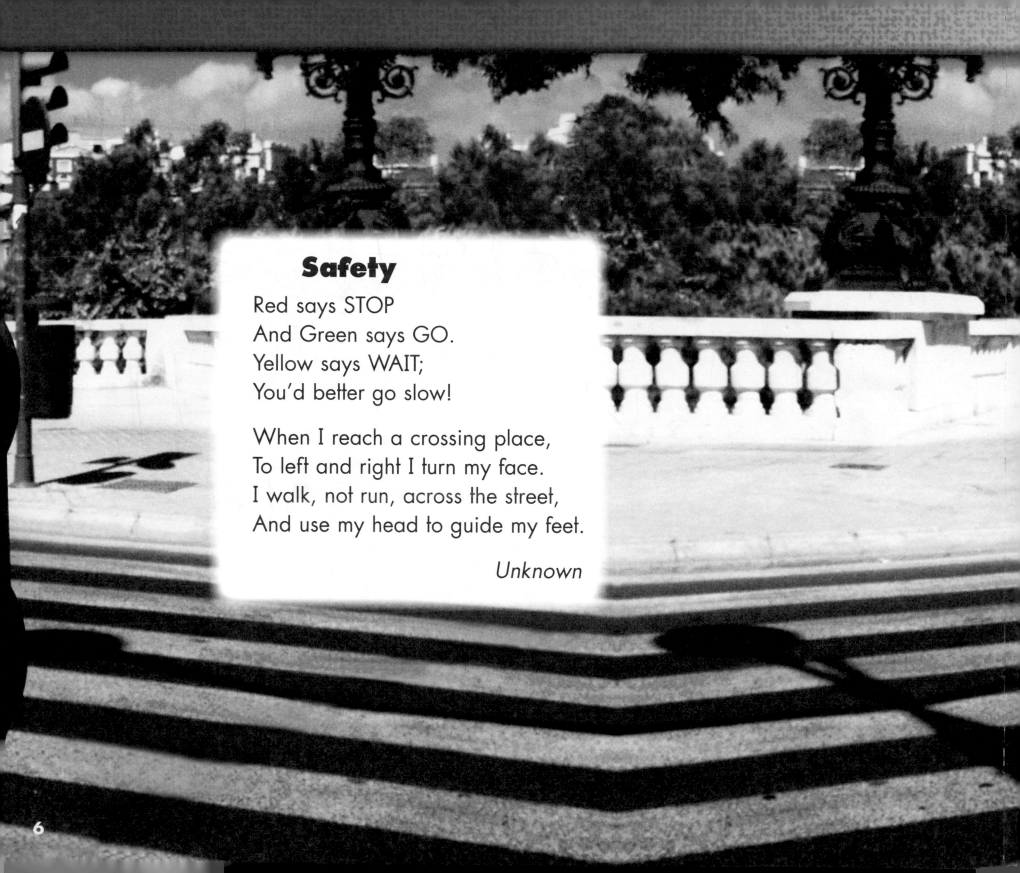

Safety

Red says STOP
And Green says GO.
Yellow says WAIT;
You'd better go slow!

When I reach a crossing place,
To left and right I turn my face.
I walk, not run, across the street,
And use my head to guide my feet.

Unknown

Pretest

Show What You Can Do

Write your name here.

Write letters you know here.

Write how old you are here.

Show what else you can write here. Draw a picture about your writing.

Letters and Numerals

A a A a B b B b C c c c D d D d

E e E e F f F f G g G g H h H h

I i I i J j J j K k K k L l L l

M m M m N n N n O o O o

Trace the uppercase letter that begins your name.
Trace the lowercase letters in your name.

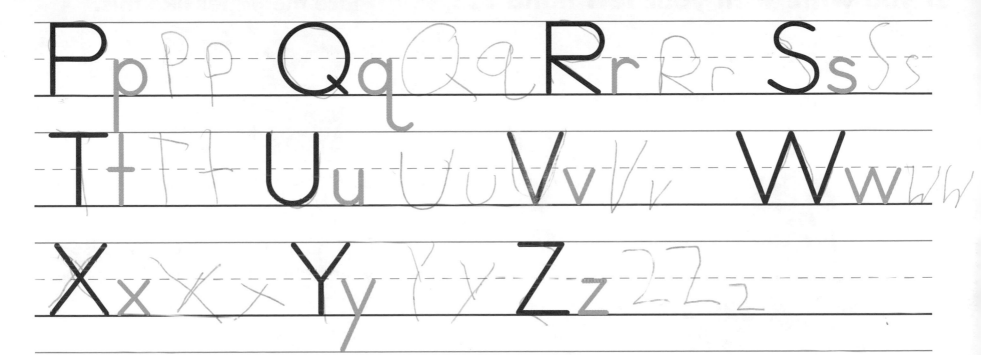

P p p p p p Q q Q q R r r r r S s s s
T t t t U u u u u V v v v v W w w w
X x x x x x Y y y y Z z z z z z

Trace the numeral that tells your age.

1 2 3 4 5 6 7 8 9 10

Write your name here.

1 2 3 4 5 6 7 8 9 10

If you write with your left hand . . .

Sit like this.

Sit comfortably. Lean forward a little.
Keep your feet flat on the floor.

Place the paper like this.

Slant the paper as shown in the picture.

Rest both arms on the desk. Use your right hand to move the paper as you write.

Pull the pencil toward your left elbow when you write.

Hold the pencil like this.

Hold the pencil with your thumb and first two fingers.

Do not squeeze the pencil when you write.

If you write with your **right** hand . . .

Sit like this.
Sit comfortably. Lean forward a little.
Keep your feet flat on the floor.

Place the paper like this.

Place the paper straight in front of you.

Rest both arms on the desk. Use your left hand to move the paper as you write.

Pull the pencil toward the middle of your body when you write.

Hold the pencil like this.

Hold the pencil with your thumb and first two fingers.

Do not squeeze the pencil when you write.

Models and Guidelines

There are writing models in your book.
The models are on guidelines.

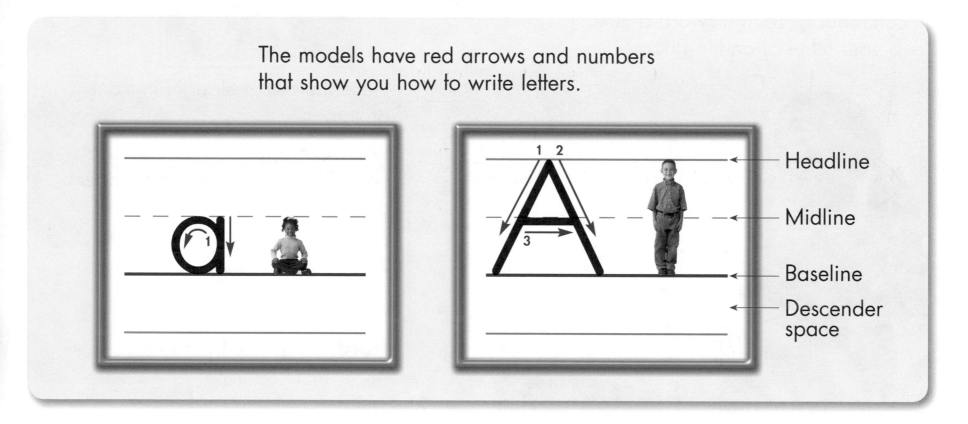

The models have red arrows and numbers
that show you how to write letters.

Headline

Midline

Baseline

Descender
space

Start at the green dot when you trace and write.

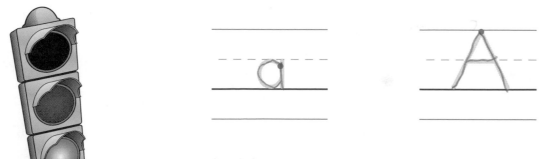

Stop and Check

You will see **Stop and Check** signs in your book when you finish a line of writing. When you see this sign, stop and circle the best letter you wrote on that line.

Circle the best letter on this line.

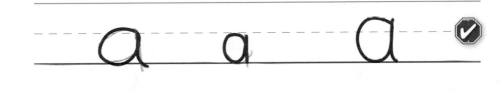

Keys to Legibility

There are four kinds of Keys in your book.
The words on the keys are **Shape, Size, Spacing,** and **Slant.**
Good writers think about these things when they write.

The Keys will help you make sure your writing is legible.
Legible means easy to read.

Vertical Lines

Some letters and numerals have lines that are straight up and down.
Trace the straight up and down lines in these letters and numerals.

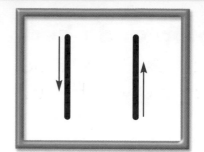

H D E t b i 9 4

Start at the green dot. ● Stop at the red dot. ●
Trace the vertical lines in the picture.

Start at the green dot. ● Stop at the red dot. ●
Trace and write. Pull down straight.

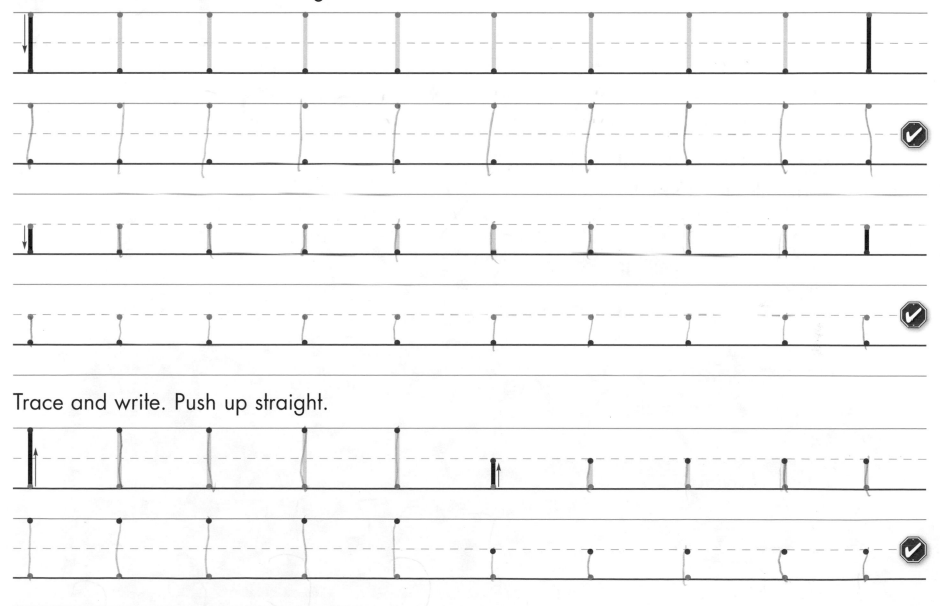

Trace and write. Push up straight.

Horizontal Lines

Some letters and numerals have lines that slide from side to side.
Trace the slide lines in these letters and numerals.

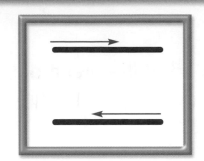

F G B z f e 5 7

Start at the green dot. ● Stop at the red dot. ●
Trace the horizontal lines in the picture.

Start at the green dot. ● Stop at the red dot. ●
Trace and write. Slide right.

Trace and write. Slide left.

Backward Circle Lines

Some letters and numerals have backward circle lines.
Trace the backward circle lines in these letters and the numeral.

O   C   Q   e   c   d   q   9

Start at the green dot. ● Stop at the red dot. ●
Trace the backward circle lines in the picture.

Trace and write. Circle back.

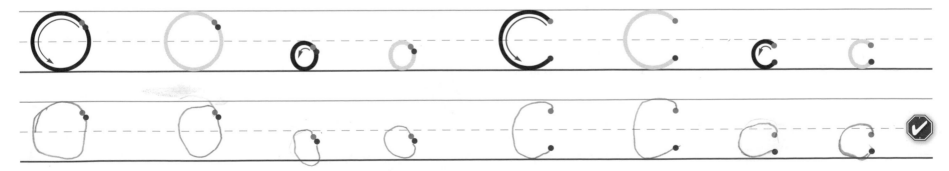

Forward Circle Lines

Some letters and numerals have forward circle lines.
Trace the forward circle lines in these letters and numerals.

R P D b 5 3

Start at the green dot. ● Stop at the red dot. ●
Trace the forward circle lines in the picture.

Trace and write. Circle forward.

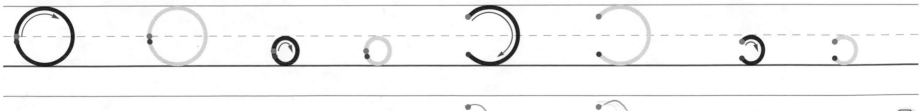

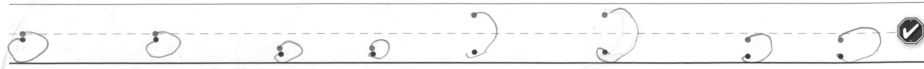

Slant Lines

Some letters and numerals have slant lines.
Trace the slant lines in these letters and numerals.

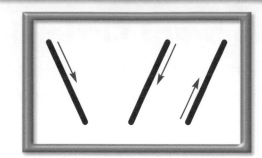

A N Q y w z 2 7

Start at the green dot. ● Stop at the red dot. ●
Trace the slant lines in the picture.

Start at the green dot. ● Stop at the red dot. ●
Trace and write. Slant right.

Trace and write. Slant left.

Trace and write. Slant up.

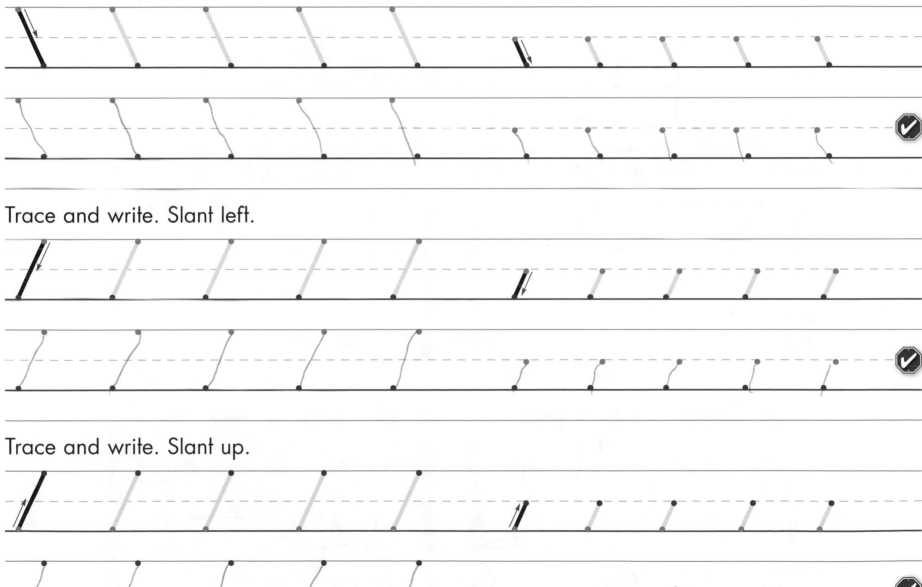

Shape

These letters have good shape!

Make your writing easy to read.
Look at the shape of each letter.

I can write letters.

Vertical Lines
Trace the I with your finger.

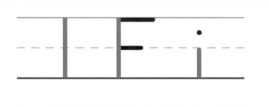

Horizontal Lines
Trace the — with your finger.

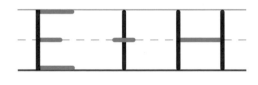

Circle Lines
Trace the O with your finger.

Slant Lines
Trace the / with your finger.

Trace the | lines in these letters.

I T P D R h p r

Trace the — lines in these letters.

E F L H G A e f

Trace the O lines in these letters.

O C S B c s o q

Trace the / \ lines in these letters.

Q X K M v w x k

25

Each letter should touch either the midline or the headline.

Make your writing easy to read.
Look at the size of each letter.

Writing is fun!

Tall Letters
Tall letters touch the headline.

K b d

Short Letters
Short letters touch the midline.

o m e

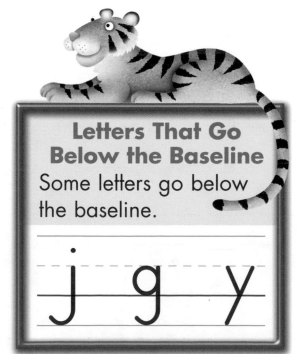

Letters That Go Below the Baseline
Some letters go below the baseline.

j g y

Start at the green dot. •
Trace and write tall letters.

T O A L D I t d

T O A L D I t d

Trace and write short letters.

a o c i e v r n

a o c i e v r n

Trace and write letters that go below the baseline.

g p j q y

g p j q y

Make your writing easy to read. Look at the spacing between letters.

These letters are too close.	These letters are too far apart.	These letters have good spacing.
close	far	good

Circle the two words with good spacing between letters.

boy   brother   sister   girl

Trace and write words. Use good spacing between letters.

aunts   uncles   cousins

Make your writing easy to read.
Look at the spacing between the words and sentences.

This is just right. This is

Write a ✔ next to the sentence that has good spacing between the words and sentences.

This is easy to read. This

Thisishardto read.Thisishardto

Write the sentence. Use good spacing between the words and sentences.

I can read. I can read.

Make your writing easy to read.
Look at the slant of the letters.

Hello, everyone!

These letters are straight up and down.

straight

Circle each word that is straight up and down.

smile smile *smile* sm*i*le

laugh laugh laugh laugh

Trace and write the words. Make the letters straight up and down.

giggle   sing   dance

hum   play

This writing is straight up and down.

Signposts

Signposts . . . signposts . . .
What do they say?
"School Ahead"
Or "Children at Play,"
"Don't Feed the Animals,"
"Slow," "For Sale,"
"Keep off the Grass,"
"Don't Lean on the Rail,"
Signposts . . . signposts . . .
Have SO much to say,
And each is important
In its very own way.

Vivian Gouled

ONE WAY

DETOUR

Writing Numerals

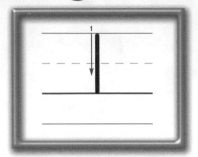

Trace and write.

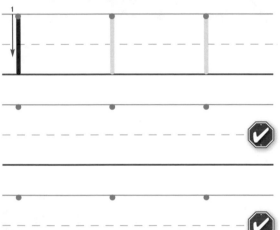

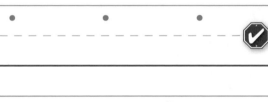

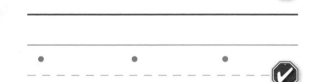

Stroke descriptions to guide numeral formation at home:

1. Pull down straight.

2. 1. Curve forward; slant left. Slide right.

3. 1. Curve forward. Curve forward.

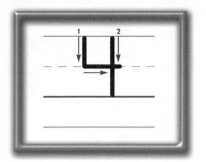

Trace and write.

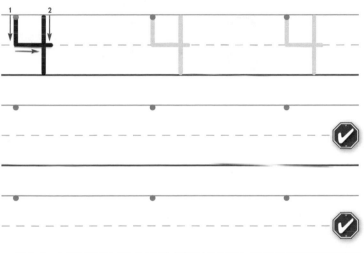

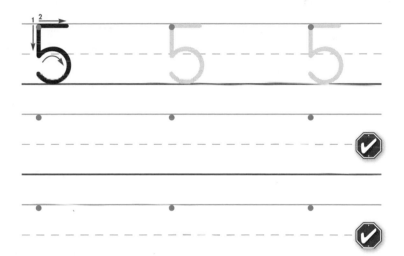

1. Pull down straight.
   Slide right. Lift.
2. Pull down straight.

1. Pull down straight.
   Circle forward. Lift.
2. Slide right.

Writing Numerals

Trace and write.

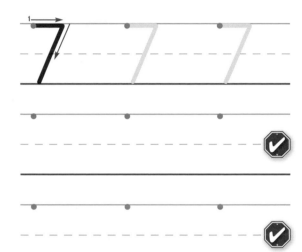

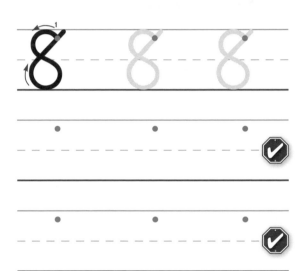

Stroke descriptions to guide numeral formation at home:

 1. Curve down; curve up and around.

 1. Slide right. Slant left.

1. Curve back; curve forward; slant up.

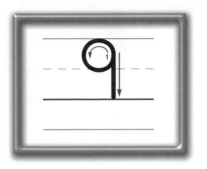

Trace and write.

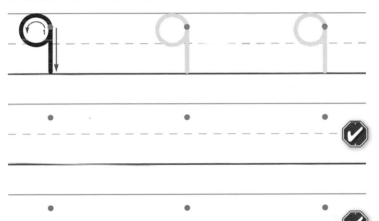

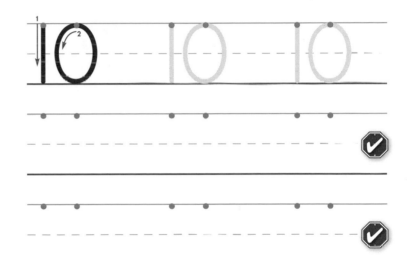

 1. Circle back all the way around. Pull down straight.

1. Pull down straight. Lift.
2. Curve down; curve up.

Writing Numerals

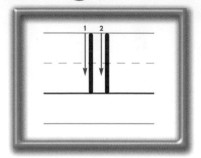

Trace and write.

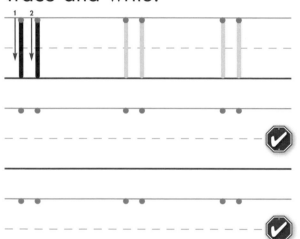
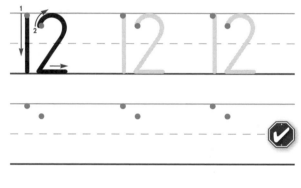
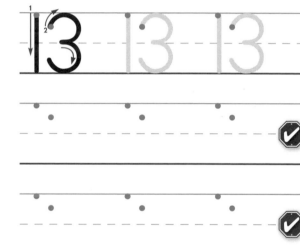

Stroke descriptions to guide numeral formation at home:

1. Pull down straight. Lift.
2. Pull down straight.

1. Pull down straight. Lift.
2. Curve forward; slant left. Slide right.

1. Pull down straight. Lift.
2. Curve forward. Curve forward.

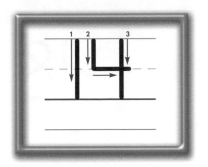

Trace and write.

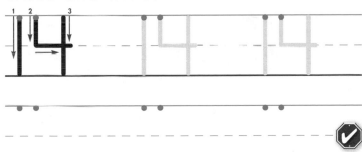

1. Pull down straight. Lift.
2. Pull down straight.
   Slide right. Lift.
3. Pull down straight.

1. Pull down straight. Lift.
2. Pull down straight.
   Circle forward. Lift.
3. Slide right.

Writing Numerals

Trace and write.

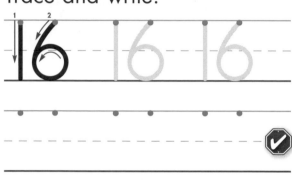 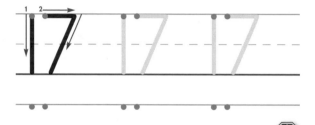 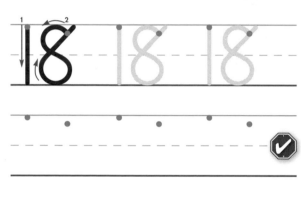

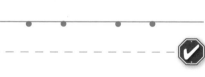 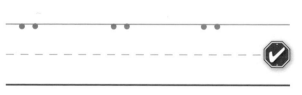 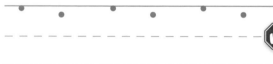

Stroke descriptions to guide numeral formation at home:

1. Pull down straight. Lift.
2. Curve down; curve up and around.

1. Pull down straight. Lift.
2. Slide right. Slant left.

1. Pull down straight. Lift.
2. Curve back; curve forward; slant up.

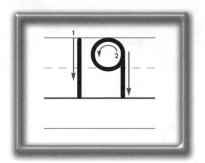

Trace and write.

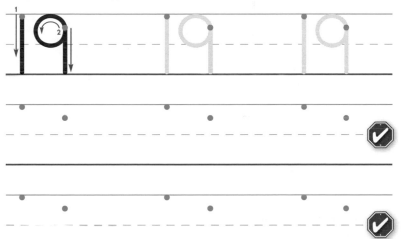

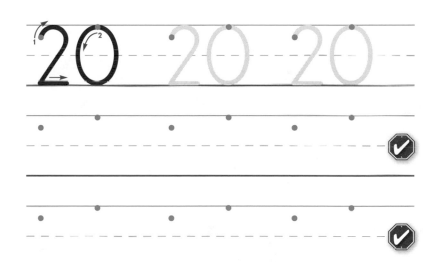

1. Pull down straight. Lift.
2. Circle back all the way around. Pull down straight.

1. Curve forward; slant left. Slide right. Lift.
2. Curve down; curve up.

Write **1 – 5**.

1   2   3   4   5

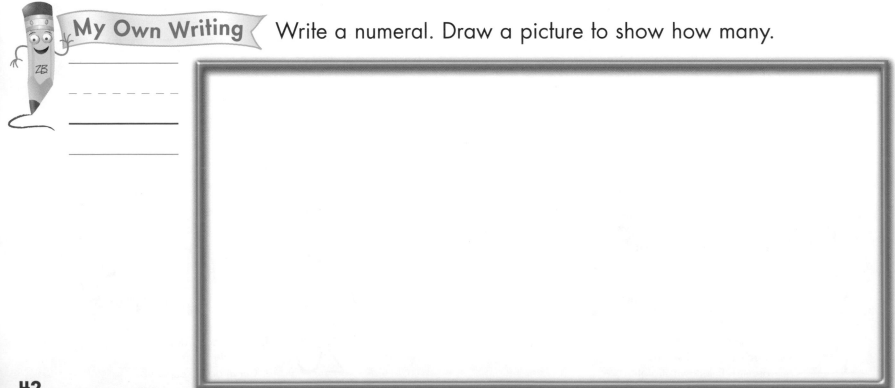

My Own Writing   Write a numeral. Draw a picture to show how many.

42

Write **6 – 10**.

6   7   8   9   10

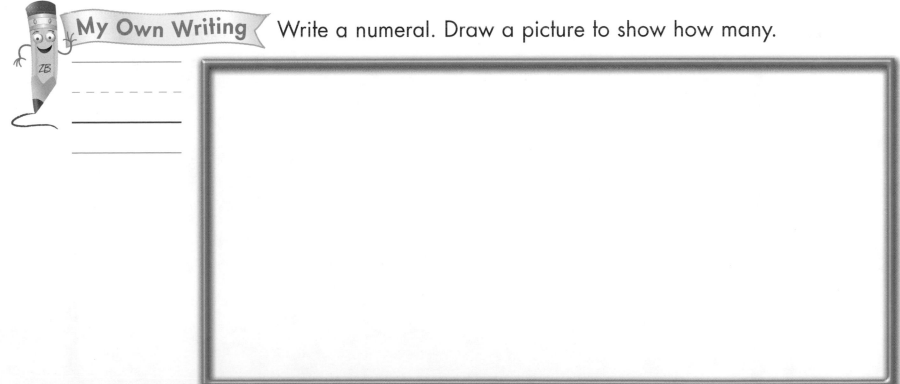

My Own Writing Write a numeral. Draw a picture to show how many.

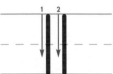

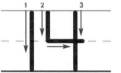

Write **11 – 15**.

11   12   13   14   15

My Own Writing   Write a numeral. Draw a picture to show how many.

Write **16** – **20**.

16 17 18 19 20

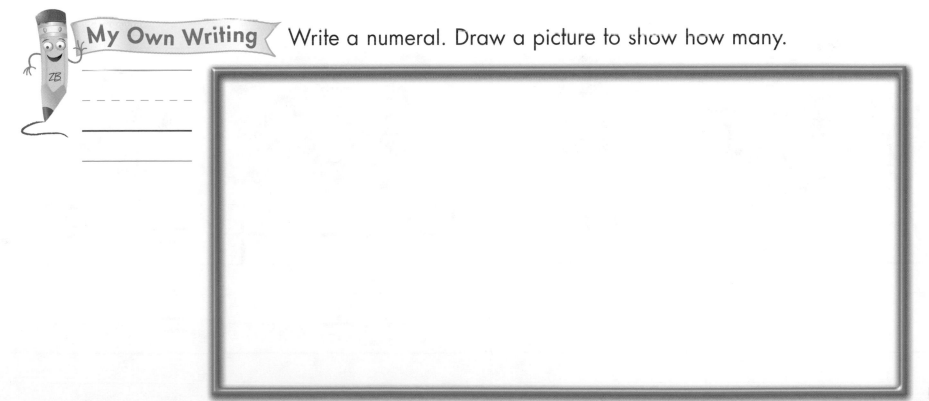

My Own Writing Write a numeral. Draw a picture to show how many.

Write the number sentences.

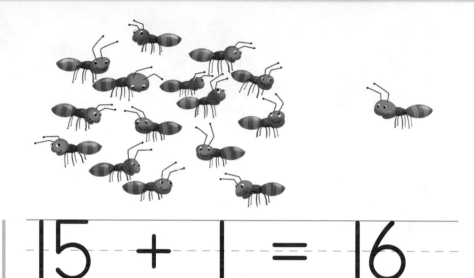

1 + 2 = 3

___ + ___ = ___

15 + 1 = 16

___ + ___ = ___

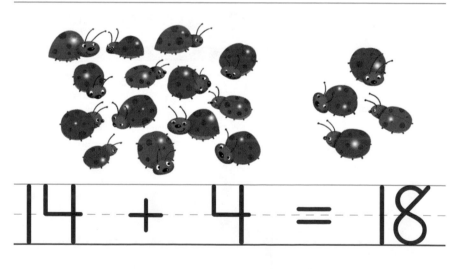

7 + 2 = 9

___ + ___ = ___

14 + 4 = 18

___ + ___ = ___

Write the number sentences.

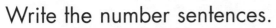

$5 - 1 = 4$

$18 - 7 = 11$

___ − ___ = ___

___ − ___ = ___

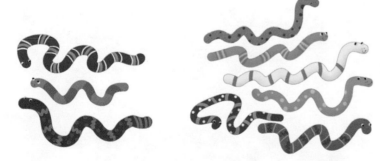

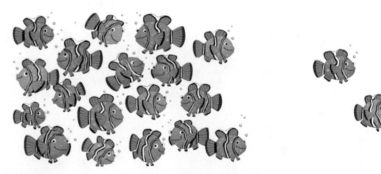

$9 - 6 = 3$

$20 - 2 = 18$

___ − ___ = ___

___ − ___ = ___

Clouds

Wonder where they come from?
Wonder where they go?
Wonder why they're sometimes high
and sometimes hanging low?
Wonder what they're made of,
and if they weigh a lot?
Wonder if the sky feels bare
up there
    when clouds are not?

                    Aileen Fisher

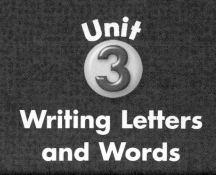

Trace and write.

l

Trace and write.

L

✓

✓

✓

✓

leaf   like

Lola   Luke

Stroke descriptions to guide letter formation at home:

1. Pull down straight.

1. Pull down straight.
   Slide right.

50

Stop and Check

Circle your best l.

Circle your best L.

Write the words.

long   lake   live   love

Write the sentence.

Look at my letters.

My Own Writing   Write a sentence that tells how your letters look.

My letters

Trace and write.

Trace and write.

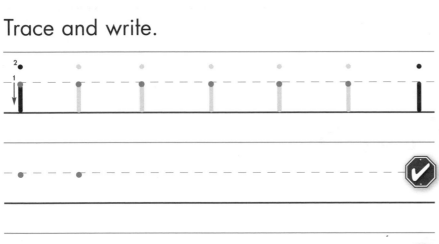 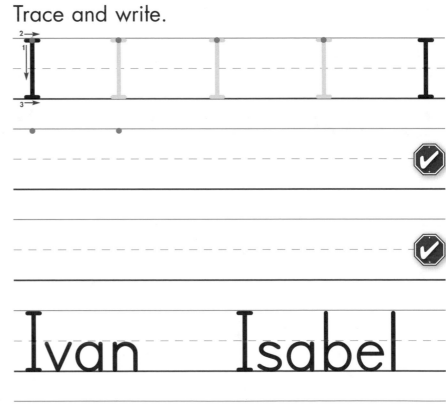

insect lit

Ivan Isabel

Stroke descriptions to guide letter formation at home:

1. Pull down straight. Lift.
2. Dot.

1. Pull down straight. Lift.
2. Slide right. Lift.
3. Slide right.

 Stop and Check
Circle your best i.
Circle your best I.

Write the words.

inch   ill   into   it

Write the sentence.

I like to write my name.

My Own Writing   Write a sentence that tells about something you like to do.

I really like

Size

Circle your best short letter.

53

Trace and write.

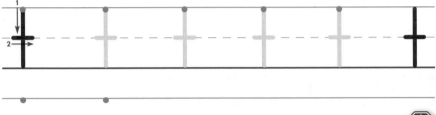

Trace and write.

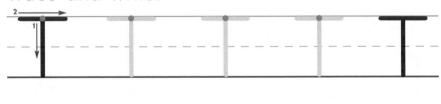

turtle talk

Tate Tara

Stroke descriptions to guide letter formation at home:

1. Pull down straight. Lift.
2. Slide right.

1. Pull down straight. Lift.
2. Slide right.

Stop and Check
Circle your best t.
Circle your best T.

Write the words.

than   table   tell   take

Write the sentence.

This is my toy train.

My Own Writing   Finish the sentence about toy trains.

Toy trains are

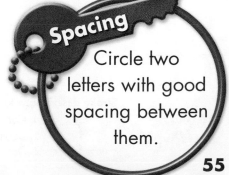

Spacing

Circle two letters with good spacing between them.

Trace and write.

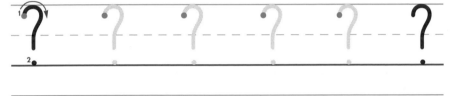

Trace and write.

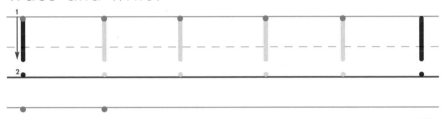

Who? Why?

Good! Wow!

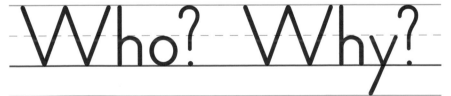
Stroke descriptions to guide letter formation at home:

1. Curve forward; pull down straight. Lift.
2. Dot.

1. Pull down straight. Lift.
2. Dot.

 Stop and Check
Circle your best ?.
Circle your best !.

Write the sentences.

Can you come over?

I will see you soon!

 My Own Writing Write words to finish the sentence.

I like to see

Slant

Circle a letter that is straight up and down.

Write the letters.

l l l l l

i i i i i

t t t t t

? ? ? ? ?

L L L

I I I

T T T

! ! ! !

Write the words.

it   lit   ill   till   little

Write the sentences.

Look at me!

Today is my birthday.

Am I one year older?

 Write a sentence about what you like to do on your birthday.

Stop and Check
Circle your best tall letter.   59

Trace and write.

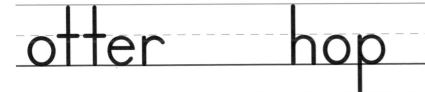

otter   hop

Trace and write.

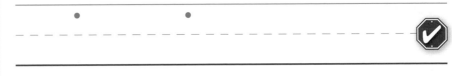

Olivia Ollie

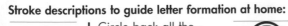

school
Home

60

Stroke descriptions to guide letter formation at home:

l. Circle back all the way around.

l. Circle back all the way around.

Stop and Check

Circle your best **o**.
Circle your best **O**.

Write the words.

octopus   off   on   odd

Write the sentence.

Our class took a trip.

My Own Writing Tell about a class trip you have taken. Use a complete sentence.

Our trip was

Shape

Circle your best letter that has a ◯ line.

61

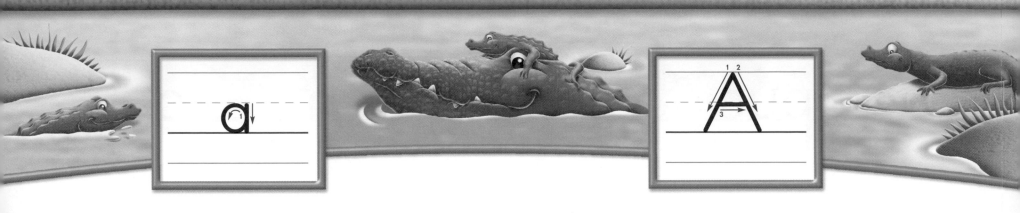

Trace and write.

a a a a a

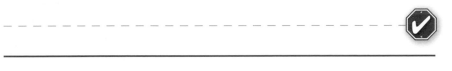

alligator act

Trace and write.

A A A A A

Ali Anna

Stroke descriptions to guide letter formation at home:

1. Circle back all the way around; push up straight. Pull down straight.

A
1. Slant left. Lift.
2. Slant right. Lift.
3. Slide right.

62

Stop and Check

Circle your best a.

Circle your best A.

Write the words.

as   animal   ask   all

Write the sentence.

All my friends play ball.

My Own Writing Write words to finish the sentence.

I can play

Size

Circle a word you wrote that has good size.

Trace and write.

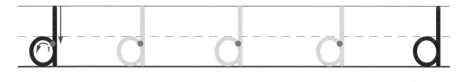

duck   dig

Trace and write.

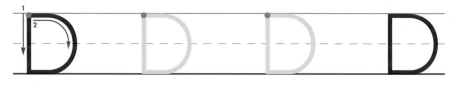

Deb   Dan

school Home

Stroke descriptions to guide letter formation at home:

1. Circle back all the way around; push up straight. Pull down straight.

1. Pull down straight. Lift.
2. Slide right; curve forward; slide left.

Stop and Check
Circle your best d.
Circle your best D.

64

Write the words.

dad   doll   dress   do

Write the sentence.

Do you like dinosaurs?

Write words to finish the sentence.

Dinosaurs are

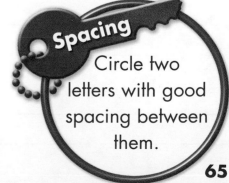

Spacing

Circle two letters with good spacing between them.

Write the letters.

o o o o   a a a a   d d d d

O O O O   A A A   D D D

Write the words.

odd   add   dad   dot

Write the naming words.

dog

toad

Dan

apple

yard

Amy

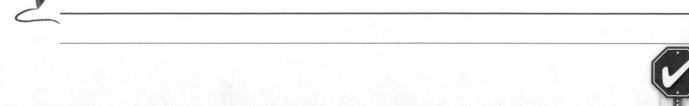

My Own Writing Write a sentence telling what you like to do with your friends.

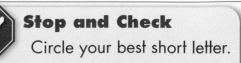

Write the story about a dog.
Make your writing easy to read.

I have a dog named Andy.

I have had him one year.

I love him more each day.

All people should have dogs.

Is your writing easy to read?

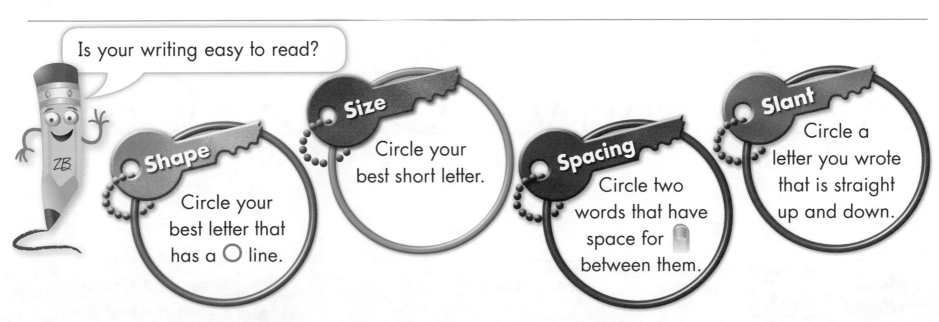

Shape
Circle your best letter that has a ○ line.

Size
Circle your best short letter.

Spacing
Circle two words that have space for between them.

Slant
Circle a letter you wrote that is straight up and down.

Trace and write.

c c c c c

Trace and write.

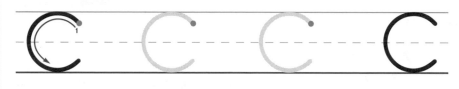

C C C C

car   carry

Carlos Cora

Stroke descriptions to guide letter formation at home:

c   1. Circle back.

C   1. Circle back.

Stop and Check

Circle your best c.
Circle your best C.

Write the words.

chest   chair   cook   cut

Write the sentence.

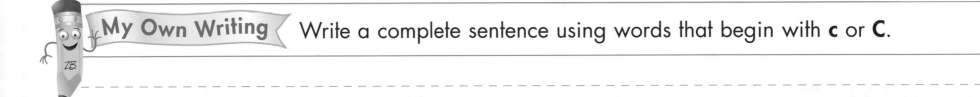
Can you count to 20?

My Own Writing   Write a complete sentence using words that begin with **c** or **C**.

Slant

Circle a
a word that is
straight up and
down.

71

Trace and write.

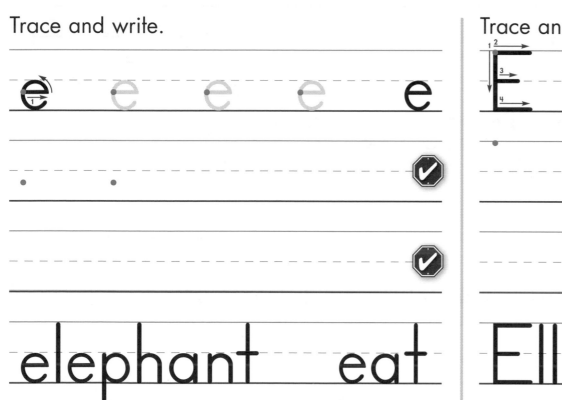

e   e   e   e   e

elephant   eat

Trace and write.

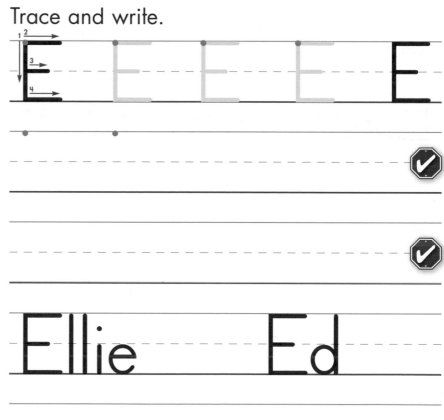

E   E   E   E   E

Ellie   Ed

School Home

72

Stroke descriptions to guide letter formation at home:

e
I. Slide right.
   Circle back.

E
I. Pull down straight. Lift.
2. Slide right. Lift.
3. Slide right; stop short. Lift.
4. Slide right.

Stop and Check
Circle your best e.
Circle your best E.

Write the words.

egg end empty each

Write the sentence.

Everyone enjoys stories.

 **My Own Writing** Write a sentence using words that have **e** or **E** in them.

Shape

Circle your best letter that has a l line.

Trace and write.

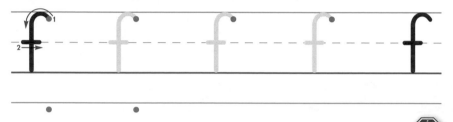

f   f   f   f   f

fish   find

Trace and write.

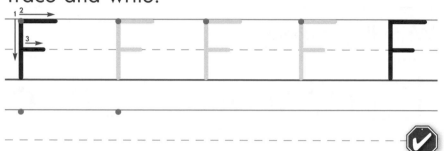

F   F   F   F   F

Fred   Flora

Stroke descriptions to guide letter formation at home:

 1. Curve back; pull down straight. Lift.
2. Slide right.

 1. Pull down straight. Lift.
2. Slide right. Lift.
3. Slide right; stop short.

 Stop and Check
Circle your best f.
Circle your best F.

Write the words.

fun   family   fall   fly

Write the sentence.

Friends have lots of fun.

 **My Own Writing** Write a complete sentence using words that begin with **f** or **F**.

Size

Circle your best tall letter.

Write the letters.

c   c   c   c   e   e   e   e   f   f   f   f

C   C   C   C   E   E   E   E   F   F   F   F

Write the words.

face   feet   ice   life

76

Write the action words.

eat

catch

call

fill

feed

color

 My Own Writing Write a sentence that tells what you like to do. Use an action word.

Trace and write.

g   g   g   g   g

✔
✔

goat   go

Trace and write.

G   G   G   G   G

✔
✔

Grace   Glen

Stroke descriptions to guide letter formation at home:

g — **I.** Circle back all the way around; push up straight. Pull down straight; curve back.

G — **I.** Circle back. Slide left.

 Stop and Check
Circle your best g.
Circle your best G.

Write the words.

girl   gate   goes   got

Write the sentence.

Get ready, get set, giggle!

My Own Writing   Write a sentence using words that begin with **g** or **G**.

Spacing

Circle two words with good spacing between them.

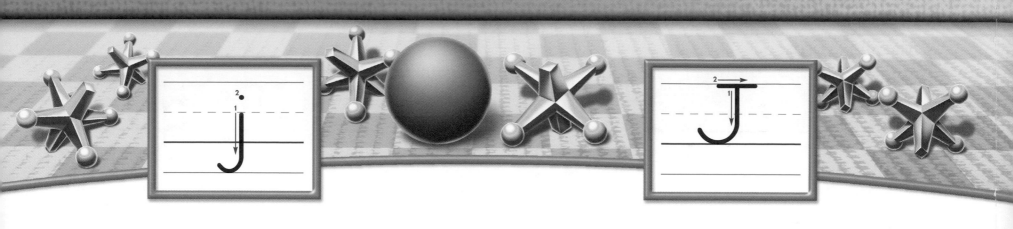

Trace and write.

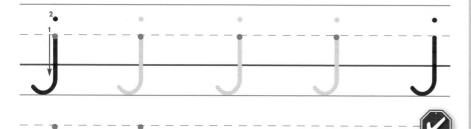

jacks   jump

Trace and write.

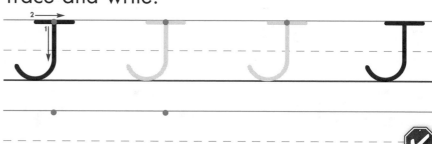

Juan   Jen

Stroke descriptions to guide letter formation at home:

1. Pull down straight; curve back. Lift.
2. Dot.

1. Pull down straight; curve back. Lift.
2. Slide right.

Stop and Check
Circle your best j.
Circle your best J.

Write the words.

jam   jar   joke   jog

Write the sentence.

Join our jumping game.

Write a complete sentence using words that begin with **j** or **J**.

Slant

Circle a letter that is straight up and down.

Trace and write.

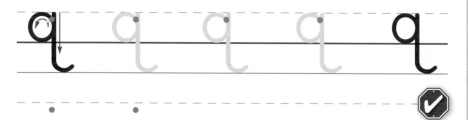

q q q q

quilt   quit

Trace and write.

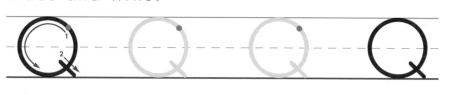

Q Q Q Q

Quita Quinn

Stroke descriptions to guide letter formation at home:

I. Circle back all the way around; push up straight. Pull down straight; curve forward.

I. Circle back all the way around. Lift.
2. Slant right.

Write the words.

queen   quart   quarter

Write the sentences. Leave the correct spacing between words and sentences.

Quick! It's time to go.

Write a sentence using words that begin with **qu** or **Qu**.

Shape

Circle your best letter that has a ⭕ line.

Write the letters.

g g g g g   j j j j j   q q q q q

G G G   J J J   Q Q Q

Write the words.

cage   jeans   grass   quite

Write the describing words.

juicy

green

good

jolly

quiet

quick

 My Own Writing Write a sentence about something you like. Use describing words.

Stop and Check
Circle your best letter.

85

Write the letter.
Make your writing easy to read.

Dear Grandpa Joe,

I would like to thank you

for the shirt and shoes.

Love,

Jorge

Is your writing easy to read?

Shape
Circle your best letter that has a — line.

Size
Circle your best tall letter.

Spacing
Circle two words that have space for ▯ between them.

Slant
Circle a word you wrote that has good slant.

Trace and write.

 u

Trace and write.

umbrella

Uri   Uma

Stroke descriptions to guide letter formation at home:

 I. Pull down straight;
curve forward; push up.
Pull down straight.

 I. Pull down straight;
curve forward; push up.

 Stop and Check
Circle your best u.
Circle your best U.

Write the words.

uncle   us   under   up

Write the sentence.

Use your umbrella now.

 My Own Writing What do you use when it rains? Write a sentence to answer the question.

Size

Circle your best short letter.

89

Trace and write.

star   see

Trace and write.

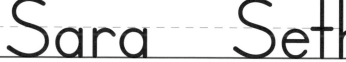

Sara   Seth

Stroke descriptions to guide letter formation at home:

s   I. Curve back;
     curve forward.

S   I. Curve back; curve forward.

Stop and Check
Circle your best s.
Circle your best S.

Write the words.

said   sun   sit   sofa

Write the sentence.

Should I sing a song?

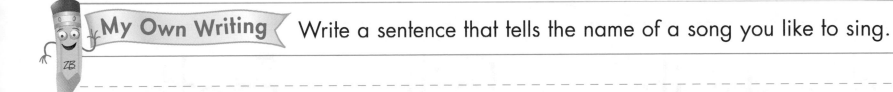 My Own Writing   Write a sentence that tells the name of a song you like to sing.

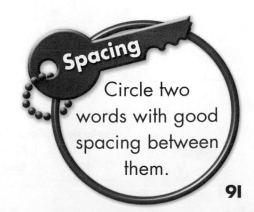

Spacing

Circle two words with good spacing between them.

91

Trace and write.

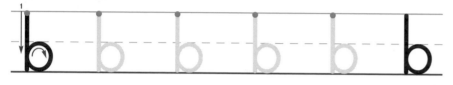

Trace and write.

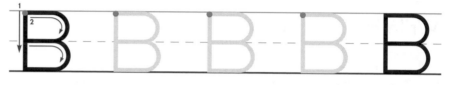

boat   build

Bill   Beth

Stroke descriptions to guide letter formation at home:

I. Pull down straight.
   Push up; circle forward.

I. Pull down straight. Lift.
2. Slide right; curve forward; slide left. Slide right; curve forward; slide left.

Stop and Check
Circle your best b.
Circle your best B.

Write the words.

bell   baby   been   bring

Write the sentence.

Big books are great!

My Own Writing   Write a sentence telling what kind of books you like.

Slant

Circle a word you wrote that has good slant.

Trace and write.

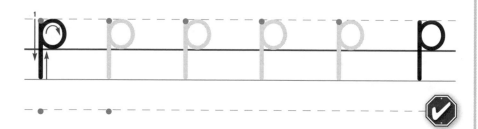

Trace and write.

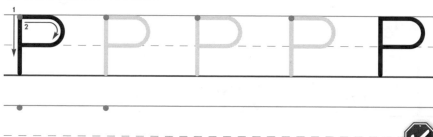

pants   pull

Pat   Pedro

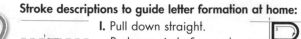
Stroke descriptions to guide letter formation at home:

p
1. Pull down straight. Push up; circle forward.

P
1. Pull down straight. Lift.
2. Slide right; curve forward; slide left.

Stop and Check
Circle your best p.
Circle your best P.

Write the words.

pen　　　pig　　　push　　　put

Write the sentence.

Please pass the paper.

 My Own Writing — Write a complete sentence that begins with **Please**.

Shape

Circle your best letter that has a l line.

Review

Write the letters.

u u u   s s s   b b b   p p p

U U   S S   B B   P P

Write the words.

bus   pup   cub   cup

bus   pup   cub   cup

96

Write the tongue twisters. Then say them fast.

Bob bakes bread.

Paula pets a pink pig.

Six snakes have snacks.

 **My Own Writing** Write your own tongue twister.

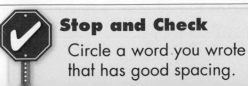 **Stop and Check**
Circle a word you wrote
that has good spacing.

Trace and write.

r r r r r r

rocket run

Trace and write.

R R R R R

Ron Rosa

Stroke descriptions to guide letter formation at home:

r 1. Pull down straight.
Push up; curve forward.

R 1. Pull down straight. Lift.
2. Slide right; curve forward;
slide left. Slant right.

Stop and Check
Circle your best r.
Circle your best R.

Write the words.

rock   rain   read   ring

Write the sentence.

Read me a story.

My Own Writing   Who reads to you? Write a sentence to answer the question.

Size

Circle a word you wrote that has good size.

Trace and write.

nest   need

Trace and write.

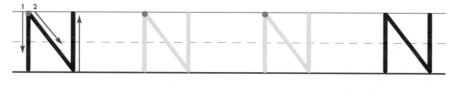

Nina   Nick

School
Home

100

Stroke descriptions to guide letter formation at home:

1. Pull down straight. Push up; curve forward; pull down straight.

1. Pull down straight. Lift.
2. Slant right. Push up straight.

Stop and Check
Circle your best n.
Circle your best N.

Write the words.

nine   nail   nap   nod

Write the sentences. Leave the correct spacing between words and sentences.

No napping! Wake up!

My Own Writing Write a sentence that tells how you wake up.

Spacing

Circle two letters with good spacing between them.

Trace and write.

m m m m **m**

marble meet

Trace and write.

M M M M **M**

Matt Ming

School Home

Stroke descriptions to guide letter formation at home:

 1. Pull down straight. Push up; curve forward; pull down straight. Push up; curve forward; pull down straight.

1. Pull down straight. Lift.
2. Slant right. Slant up. Pull down straight.

Stop and Check

Circle your best **m**.
Circle your best **M**.

102

Write the words.

mom   moon   mail   miss

Write the sentence.

My lunch is yummy!

 **My Own Writing** Tell what you like to eat for lunch. Use a complete sentence.

Slant

Circle a letter that is straight up and down.

Trace and write.

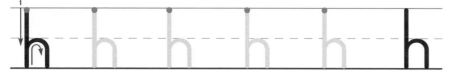

horse   hug

Trace and write.

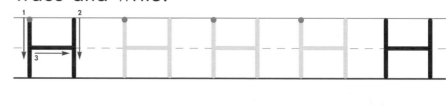

Hailey   Hank

Stroke descriptions to guide letter formation at home:

 1. Pull down straight.
Push up; curve forward;
pull down straight.

 1. Pull down straight. Lift.
2. Pull down straight. Lift.
3. Slide right.

School Home

104

Stop and Check
Circle your best h.
Circle your best H.

Write the words.

hill   house   have   hop

Write the sentence.

How may I help you?

My Own Writing   How do you help others? Write a sentence to answer the question.

Shape

Circle a word you wrote that has good shape.

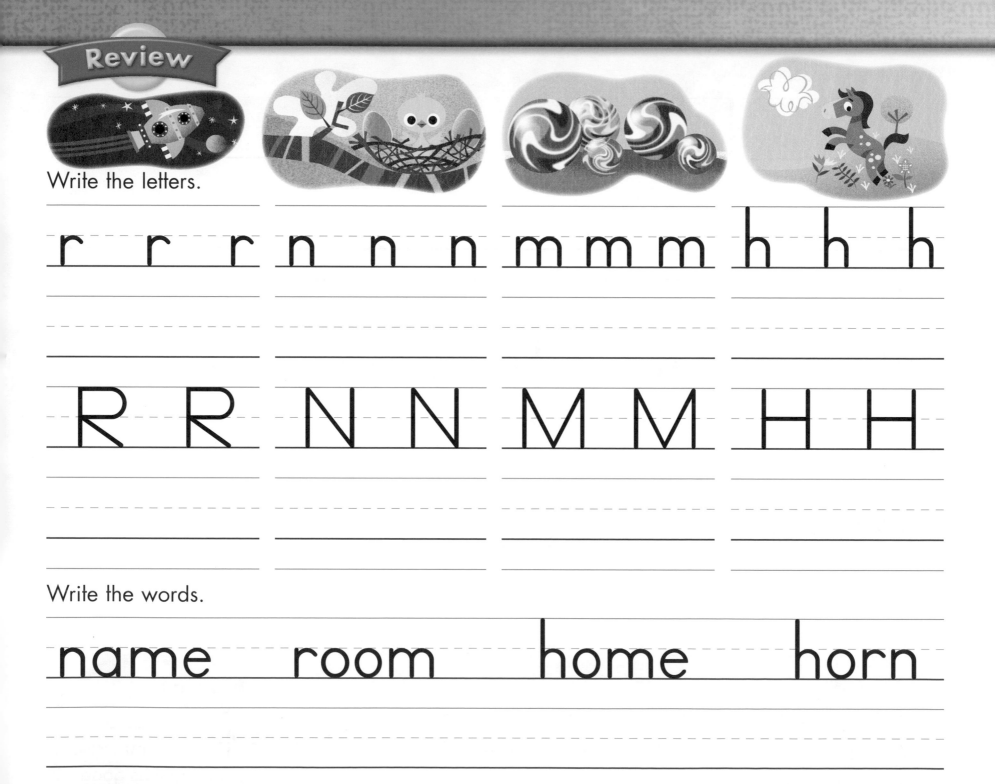

Write the letters.

r r r   n n n   m m m   h h h

R R R   N N N   M M M   H H H

Write the words.

name room home horn

Write the list of things to do.

1. Return Nate's hat.

2. Make a map.

3. Have a snack.

 My Own Writing Write one more thing to do.

4.

Slant
Spacing
Size
Shape

Write the rhyming words.
Make your writing easy to read.

rest   nest   rod   nod

rug   mug   rat   mat

nap   map   noon   moon

I see a mouse in my house!

Is your writing easy to read?

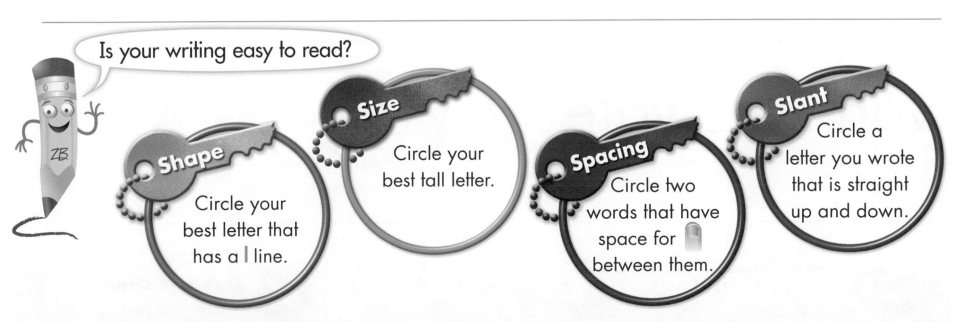

Shape Circle your best letter that has a I line.

Size Circle your best tall letter.

Spacing Circle two words that have space for between them.

Slant Circle a letter you wrote that is straight up and down.

Trace and write.

v v v v v

van   vote

Trace and write.

V V V V V

Vic   Viv

Stroke descriptions to guide letter formation at home:

 I. Slant right. Slant up.

V I. Slant right. Slant up.

Stop and Check
Circle your best v.
Circle your best V.

Write the words.

vest   video   visit   very

Write the sentence.

Violet loves vegetables.

My Own Writing Write a sentence that tells what you love to eat.

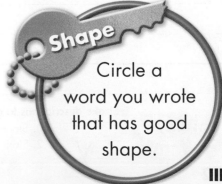

Shape

Circle a word you wrote that has good shape.

Trace and write.

yo-yo yawn

Trace and write.

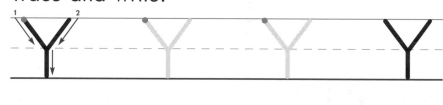

Yoko Yoshi

Stroke descriptions to guide letter formation at home:

1. Slant right. Lift.
2. Slant left.

1. Slant right. Lift.
2. Slant left. Pull down straight.

Stop and Check
Circle your best y.
Circle your best Y.

Write the words.

yard   you   yell   yes

Write the sentence.

You can play with me.

My Own Writing Write a sentence that tells what games you like to play.

Size

Circle your best letter that goes below the baseline.

Trace and write.

wagon   wait

Trace and write.

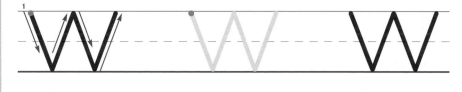

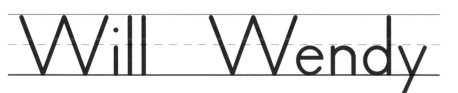

Will Wendy

Stroke descriptions to guide letter formation at home:

w **I.** Slant right. Slant up.
Slant right. Slant up.

W **I.** Slant right. Slant up.
Slant right. Slant up.

Stop and Check
Circle your best w.
Circle your best W.

Write the words.

winter   word   want   wish

Write the sentence.

Will it snow today?

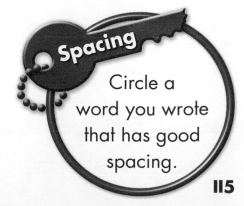

My Own Writing   Write a sentence that tells what the weather is like today.

Spacing

Circle a word you wrote that has good spacing.

Write the letters.

v v v   y y y   w w w

V V V   Y Y Y   W W W

Write the words.

your   wave   vet   way

Write the invitation.

You're Invited to a Party!

When: Friday at 4:00

Where: Valley School

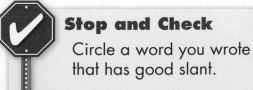

Stop and Check

Circle a word you wrote that has good slant.

117

Trace and write.

x x x x x

fox   mix

Trace and write.

X X X X

Xena Xavier

Stroke descriptions to guide letter formation at home:

 1. Slant right. Lift.
2. Slant left.

 1. Slant right. Lift.
2. Slant left.

✓ **Stop and Check**
Circle your best x.
Circle your best X.

Write the words.

box   six   taxi   fix

Write the sentence.

X marks the spot.

My Own Writing Write a sentence to tell where you would hide a treasure.

Slant

Circle a word that is straight up and down.

Trace and write.

k k k k k

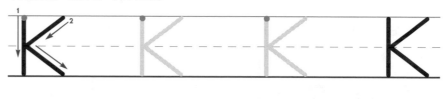

K K K K K

kite   keep

Ken   Keisha

Stroke descriptions to guide letter formation at home:

 1. Pull down straight. Lift.
2. Slant left. Slant right.

1. Pull down straight. Lift.
2. Slant left. Slant right.

Stop and Check
Circle your best k.
Circle your best K.

Write the words.

kids   keys   kick   kiss

Write the sentence.

Kids like to fly kites.

My Own Writing   Write a sentence that tells about other things kids like to do.

Shape

Circle your best letter that has a / line.

Trace and write.

z   z   z   z   z

Trace and write.

Z   Z   Z   Z   Z

zebra   zip

Zoey   Zach

Stroke descriptions to guide letter formation at home:

 1. Slide right. Slant left.
Slide right.

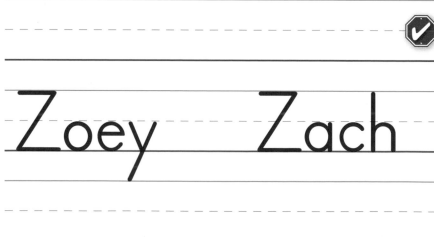 1. Slide right. Slant left.
Slide right.

 Stop and Check
Circle your best z.
Circle your best Z.

Write the words.

zoo   fuzzy   maze   zoom

Write the sentence.

Z is a zigzag letter.

My Own Writing Write a sentence that tells about things that zigzag.

Size

Circle a word you wrote that has good size.

123

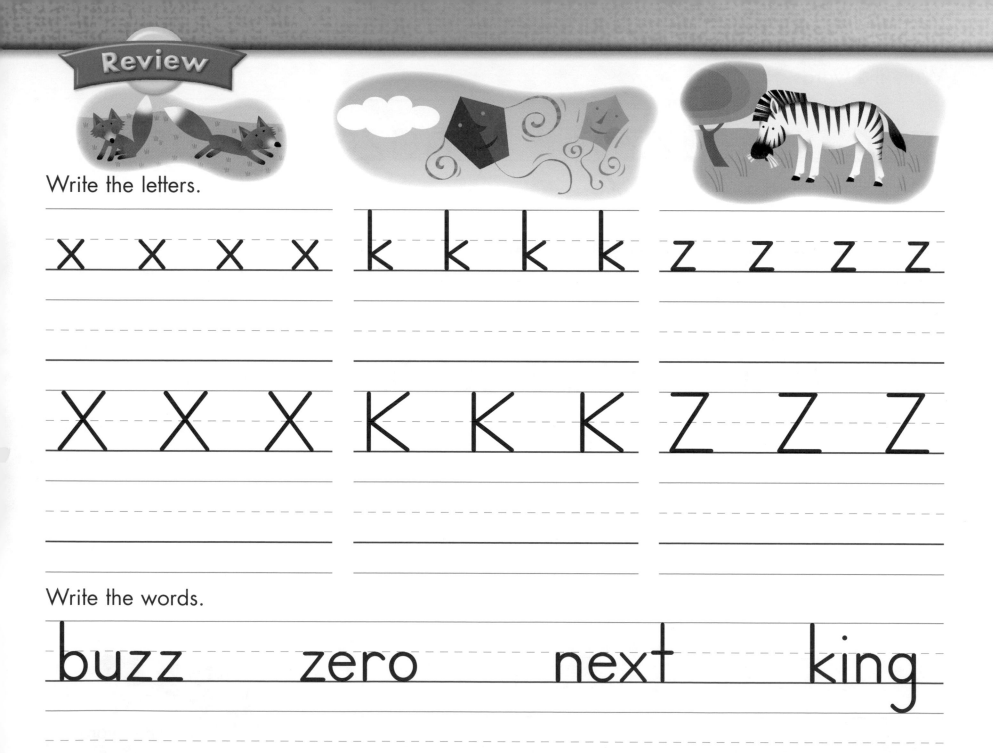

Write the letters.

x x x x   k k k k   z z z z

X X X   K K K   Z Z Z

Write the words.

buzz   zero   next   king

124

Write the sentences.

Mix the batter.

Bake the cookie.

It zooms away.

My Own Writing Write words about the Cookie Man.

Stop and Check

Circle a word you wrote that has good slant.

Write how to get ready for bed.
Make your writing easy to read.

1. Change your clothes.

2. Brush your teeth.

3. Then lie down.

Sweet dreams. ZZZzzz

Is your writing easy to read?

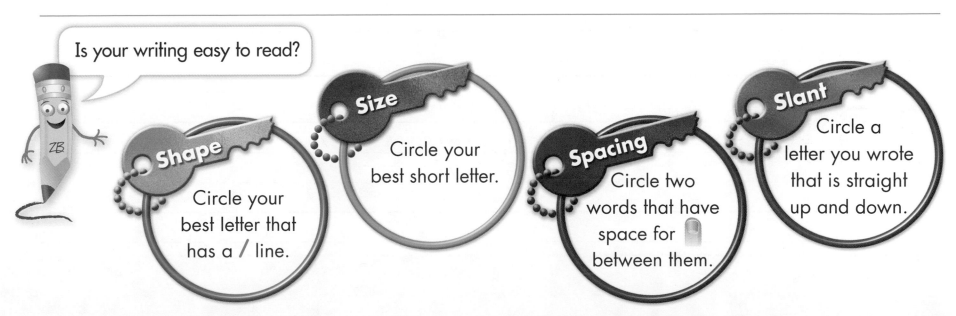

Shape
Circle your best letter that has a / line.

Size
Circle your best short letter.

Spacing
Circle two words that have space for ▯ between them.

Slant
Circle a letter you wrote that is straight up and down.

Show What You Can Do

I can write lowercase letters from **a** to **z**.

I can write uppercase letters from **A** to **Z**.

Finish the story.

Once when I was little,

I went to

The Swing

How do you like to go up in a swing,
    Up in the air so blue?
Oh, I do think it the pleasantest thing
    Ever a child can do!

Up in the air and over the wall,
    Till I can see so wide,
River and trees and cattle and all
    Over the countryside—

Till I look down on the garden green,
    Down on the roof so brown—
Up in the air I go flying again,
    Up in the air and down!

Robert Louis Stevenson

Number Words Write the numerals and the number words in English and Spanish.

1 one uno   2 two dos

3 three tres   4 four cuatro

5 five cinco

My Own Writing Write the Spanish words for **3** and **4**.

6 six seis   7 seven siete

8 eight ocho   9 nine nueve

10 ten diez

My Own Writing Write the numeral and a number word to tell your age.

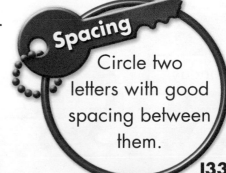

Spacing

Circle two letters with good spacing between them.

Days of the Week

Write the name of each day.

Monday   Tuesday

Wednesday   Thursday

Friday   Saturday   Sunday

Monday

Tuesday

Wednesday

Thursday

Friday

Saturday

Sunday

Friendly Letter Write to a friend. Finish this letter.

Dear _____ ,

Today is _____

_____

_____

_____

Your friend, _____

_____

_____

Slant

Circle a letter that is straight up and down.

Months

Write the name of each month.

January   February

March   April   May

June   July   August

September   October

November   December

 **My Own Writing** Write the names of two holiday months.

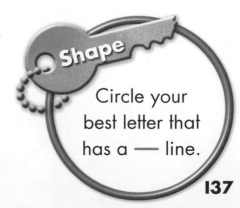
Shape

Circle your best letter that has a — line.

137

Book Review Finish this book review.

I read _____

It was about _____

I liked it because _____

Draw a Picture Draw something from the book you read.

...ke your writing easy to read.
Write this rhyme.

Rain, rain, go away.
Come again another day.

Now write it again. Try to write faster this time.

Write the rhyme one more time. Try to write faster.
Make sure your writing is easy to read.

Now read your writing. Ask others to read it, too.
Then circle Yes or No next to each sentence.

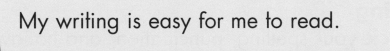

My writing is easy for me to read.	Yes	No
My writing is easy for others to read.	Yes	No

...iting and the Writing Process

...about an animal you would like to see.
...rite on a piece of writing paper. Follow these five steps as you write.

1. Prewriting
Plan ideas for your writing.
Use good handwriting so you can read your ideas later.

2. Drafting
Write your ideas in sentences.
Your writing should be easy to read.

3. Revising
Revise your writing.
Make changes so that your writing says what you mean.

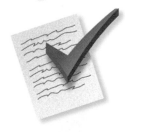

4. Editing
Check your spelling, punctuation, and handwriting.
Make sure your writing is easy to read.

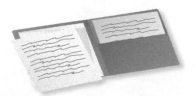

5. Publishing
Share your writing with others.
Use your best handwriting.

Record of Student's Handwriting Skills

Manuscript

	Needs Improvement	Shows Mastery		Needs Improvement	Shows Mastery
Uses good sitting position	☐	☐	Writes **e** and **E**	☐	☐
Positions paper correctly	☐	☐	Writes **f** and **F**	☐	☐
Holds pencil correctly	☐	☐	Writes **g** and **G**	☐	☐
Writes vertical lines	☐	☐	Writes **j** and **J**	☐	☐
Writes horizontal lines	☐	☐	Writes **q** and **Q**	☐	☐
Writes backward circle lines	☐	☐	Writes **u** and **U**	☐	☐
Writes forward circle lines	☐	☐	Writes **s** and **S**	☐	☐
Writes slant lines	☐	☐	Writes **b** and **B**	☐	☐
Writes numerals **1–10**	☐	☐	Writes **p** and **P**	☐	☐
Writes numerals **11–20**	☐	☐	Writes **r** and **R**	☐	☐
Writes **l** and **L**	☐	☐	Writes **n** and **N**	☐	☐
Writes **i** and **I**	☐	☐	Writes **m** and **M**	☐	☐
Writes **t** and **T**	☐	☐	Writes **h** and **H**	☐	☐
Writes **?**	☐	☐	Writes **v** and **V**	☐	☐
Writes **!**	☐	☐	Writes **y** and **Y**	☐	☐
Writes **o** and **O**	☐	☐	Writes **w** and **W**	☐	☐
Writes **a** and **A**	☐	☐	Writes **x** and **X**	☐	☐
Writes **d** and **D**	☐	☐	Writes **k** and **K**	☐	☐
Writes **c** and **C**	☐	☐	Writes **z** and **Z**	☐	☐